I spent the first half of my working life serving as a physician, a geriatrician—a specialist in the care of the old. Years spent in the company of very old people helped me grasp a handful of deep truths about life, love, and happiness.

These elders showed me how, given sufficient time, even the smallest changes can remake us.

There are, in my opinion, few things more soulful than being a patient and faithful companion of the very old, the frail, and the infirm. My patients helped me accept who I was, who I am, and who I am becoming.

- Dr. Bill Thomas

Published by Sana Publications
Editor, Kavan Peterson
714 N. Aurora St, Ithaca, NY 14850

Acknowledgements: Special thanks to Jude Meyers Thomas, Kyrié Sue Carpenter, Jeseph Meyers and Megan Pugh for this book's exquisite design.

Thomas, William H., M.D.

Philosophae Naturalis : Principia Senescentis William H. Thomas.

ISBN 978-0-9896011-3-9
1. Nonfiction
2. Aged–Care
3. Longevity–Social Aspects
4. Health Care–Gerontology
5. Aging
6. Health Care Reform

The text for this book is set in P22 Franklin Caslon
Manufactured in the United States

PHILOSOPHIÆ
NATURALIS
PRINCIPIA
SENESCENTIS.

AUTHOR
WILLIAM H. THOMAS, M.D.

Imprimatur SANA Publications.

Ithaca, New York
Anno MMXVI.

THIS BOOK IS DEDICATED TO
THOSE WHO WOULD DARE TO
INVENT A NEW OLD AGE.

We are witnesses to a world-historic achievement. We have made what was once a rarity—entry into old age—into something quite, ordinary. Hundreds of millions of people expect to grow old and will very likely do so. Even better, we have fashioned an old age that routinely yields the happiest years of one's life.

At the same time, we work ceaselessly to snatch defeat from the jaws of this great victory.

Our times are defined, in part, by a widespread and perilous aging illiteracy. We are told that old age brings only a boring conformity. We are told that aging narrows our range of experiences and diminishes our value. In fact, the opposite is true. People commonly believe and repeat a range of myths, falsehoods and stereotypes about human aging and are unable to answer the most basic questions about the nature of independence and longevity.

Principia Senescentis examines the true nature of human aging and exposes the modern mythology that places independence at the heart of dignity.

❧ CONTENTS ❧

CHAPTER I
AN INDEPENDENCE REVOLUTION

CHAPTER II
THE NATURE OF AGING

CHAPTER III
THE POWER OF
PERSONAL CONTROL

CHAPTER IV
THE EXPECTATION
OF INDEPENDENCE

CHAPTER V
OUR EXPERIENCE
WITH INDEPENDENCE

✎ CONTENTS ❧

CHAPTER VI
DISTRESSING GAPS

CHAPTER VII
THE RIGHT SHIFT

CHAPTER VIII
THE LEFT SHIFT

CHAPTER IX
LOOKING
IN THE MIRROR

CHAPTER X
NAVIGATING TO A
NEW REALITY

CHAPTER I
INDEPENDENCE REVOLUTION

Multi-Generational Reciprocity

The world is racing toward
a future that is — old.

[Figure 1: Eye of Horus]

Each new day draws us deeper into an undiscovered country where old people outnumber children under five. Of all the people who ever reached the age of 65, half are alive today.

As Proust wisely observed,

> "THE REAL VOYAGE OF DISCOVERY IS NOT SEEKING NEW LANDS BUT SEEING WITH NEW EYES."

It was old age that brought the first great engine of human progress into being. Our discovery and refinement of longevity gave us the gift of culture, spurred our development as tool-makers and made us distinctly human.

This is the invention that made all other inventions possible.

A. Adults caring for elders.
B. Elders assisting adults.

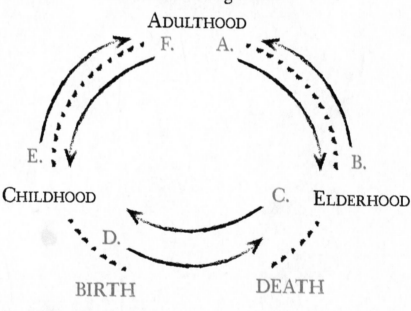

E. Children helping
   adults.
F. Adults caring
   for children.

C. Children gentled
   by elders.
D. Elders being
   revered by children.

[Figure 2: The Engine of Reciprocity]

Aging is powerful and it inspires fear as well as respect, often in equal measure.

For tens of thousands of years, this complex pattern of reciprocity has shaped us, served us, blunted our worst tendencies, and magnified our best. Given the terrible might of modern industrial society, it would seem that we need it more than ever before.

The wisdom of multi-generational social structures is undeniable, global and deserving of a word of its own.

Independence Revolution
A movement capable of creating well-being for people of all ages by strengthening and improving the means by which

(1) the young protect, sustain, and nurture their elders, and

(2) elders contribute richly to the well-being of the young.

Some would dismiss this ambition as naive optimism.

We do not.

Aging lies deep within the marrow of our bones.

Among all the creatures on this green earth,
we alone have discovered and made use of the
plenteous virtues hidden within the necessity of
growing old.

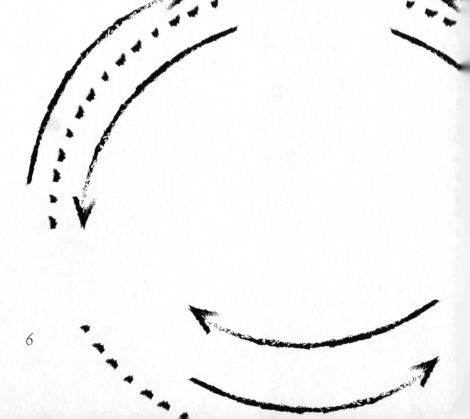

Contemporary critics of aging often claim that growing old is a luxury we can no longer afford. The most short-sighted among them want us to abandon the ancient patterns of exchange that connect the young and the very young to the old and the very old.

They forget that

WISDOM

OUTWEIGHS

WEALTH

Human longevity, rightly understood, is not the problem; it is where we will find the solutions we seek.

CHAPTER II
The Nature of Aging

$$y = 1 - 0.1(x - 28)$$

Despite aging's epochal influence over the development of homo sapiens and the course of our shared global history, we live in an era defined, in part, by a widespread (and perilous) aging illiteracy.

People commonly believe and repeat a range of myths, falsehoods and stereotypes about aging and are often unable to answer the most basic questions about its true nature. For example, few Americans are able to correctly answer this simple question:

WHY DOES THE MORTALITY RATE RISE WITH AGE?

Annual risk of death (1 in x) by age

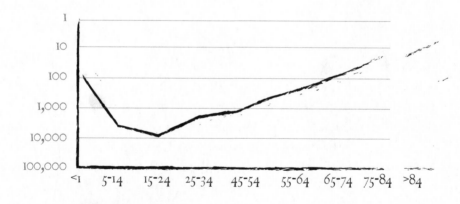

[Figure 3: Graph of Mortality Rate versus Age]

Source:
medicine.ox.ac.uk/bandolier/booth/risk/dyingage.html

This question was first addressed in a quantitative way by Bernard Strehler and Albert Mildvan in a less than cheerful, 1960 Science article titled:

GENERAL THEORY OF MORTALITY AND AGING

In the crisp vernacular of scientific understatement, Strehler and Mildvan defined "vitality" as the "capacity of an individual organism to stay alive." (Most people think of it simply as a talent for not dying). Then they asked:

WHY DOES VITALITY WANE WITH AGE?

To answer that question Strehler and Mildvan dug into a massive collection of physiological testing data gathered from adults of all ages.

WHAT THEY DISCOVERED SURPRISED THEM.

Instead of falling apart,
one way then another.
Instead of falling upon the world,
like snow.
We grow old.

Strehler and Mildvan discovered aging to be a
harmonious pattern of change that echoes across the
decades of an adult human's life.

The shift from a physiology organized around
maturation to one defined by aging occurs very close
to our 28th birthday.

How long have you been aging?

YOUR AGE − 28 =
YEARS YOU HAVE
BEEN AGING

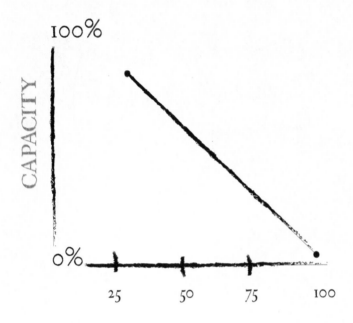

[Figure 4: Physiological Capacity Against Age]

The most popular myths portray aging as a chaotic, discordant process. Most people assume that they will be (vaguely) young for a very long time and only "get old" near the very end of their lives.

The slope of Strehler and Mildvan's line tells a different story. Between the ages of 28 and 108 we age at a remarkably consistent rate.

The centenarian ages at the same rate as the 30-year-old. The difference between them is due entirely to the amount of aging each has accumulated.

13

BUT WHAT ABOUT VITALITY?

WHAT ABOUT OUR TALENT
FOR STAYING ALIVE?

HOW AND WHY DOES THAT
CHANGE ACROSS THE LIFESPAN?

Once again, Strehler and Mildvan have an answer.

All dynamic and self-balancing systems have reserve capacities. In the context of human health and well-being, reserve capacities enable organisms that have been placed under stress return to homeostasis.

In youth, our bodies are well supplied with the energy we need to contain and overcome the stressors forced upon us by our environment.

AS WE AGE, THIS RESERVE
CAPACITY DECLINES BY
ABOUT 1% EACH YEAR.

A BAG OF GOLD COINS

Much of the experience we call "aging" is
defined by a gradual, coordinated diminishment
of the body's cognitive and physiological reserve
capacities. This process extends across three
quarters of the human lifespan.

It is almost as if, each and every morning, we wake
to find a bag of gold coins on our bedside table.
Those coins represent that day's supply of energy.

In our youth, the bag bulges with coins and we
scatter them freely and often thoughtlessly. The
young are secure in the knowledge that, when
they wake, the bag will once again be full to
overflowing.

As we mature, we find fewer coins at our bedside
and we begin to think about how they
should be spent.

Old age grants us a precious few
of these coins and elders must
carefully consider how best to
invest them.

THIS IS NORMAL.

15

Popular mythology defines old age as a litany of losses, compounding grief and inescapable sadness. Research tells a different story.

AGING BRINGS US HAPPINESS

Because aging is a gradual process, it gives us the time we need to adapt to change. Most people learn to live full and satisfying lives within the smaller reserve capacity afforded by old age.

For millions of people, normal human aging is defined by change in the direction of:

MORE HAPPINESS,
LESS ANGER AND SHAME
AND A DEEPER SENSE OF
WELL-BEING.

DOES THIS
SEEM
IMPOSSIBLE?

YES

☐

NO

☐

17

In 2010, Arthur A. Stone and Joseph E. Schwartz asked 340,847 people in the United States (between the ages 18 to 85) the following question:

> "Please imagine a ladder with steps numbered from 0 at the bottom to 10 at the top. The top of the ladder represents the best possible life for you, and the bottom of the ladder represents the worst possible life for you. On which step of the ladder would you say you personally feel you stand at this time?"

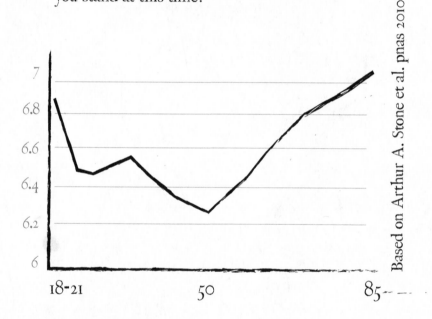

[Figure 5: Global Well-Being Ladder]

The so-called "U-Bend" of happiness hits bottom around age 50 and then begins a decades long rise.

A peculiar alchemy lies at the heart of aging.

Our ability to enjoy life
waxes even as our talent for
staying alive wanes.

This new
Happiness
and the gradual
acceptance of
Mortality,

are not unrelated.

SO WHY ARE OLD PEOPLE MORE LIKELY TO DIE THAN YOUNG PEOPLE?

When chance, in the form of an illness or injury, pushes our physiology outside of the box created by our reserve capacity, we come to the end of our lives.

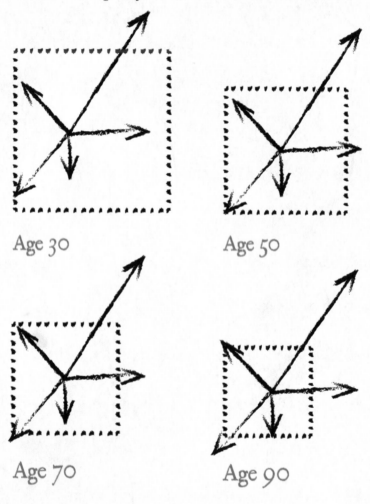

Age 30   Age 50

Age 70   Age 90

[Figure 6: Squares of Reserve]

Each box represents the reserve capacity (vitality) remaining at a given age. Each arrow represents an environmental stress. The longer the arrow, the greater the stress. From longest to shortest, the arrows represent the following situations:

- Being run over by a bus.
- Having a major heart attack.
- Contracting influenza.
- Falling while climbing out of the bathtub.
- Catching a cold.

The Law of Averages insists that, on any given day, people living with a smaller reserve capacity will be more likely to encounter a fatal stressor than people living with a larger reserve capacity.

THIS IS WHY THE MORTALITY RATE RISES WITH AGE.

WHO KNEW THE GRIM REAPER
WAS A STATISTICIAN?

Strehler and Mildvan knew:

$$ln\ a = ln\ K - (1/B)b$$

CHAPTER III
THE POWER OF PERSONAL CONTROL

Independence as Virtue

We live in a nation expressly founded upon a declaration of independence—and it shows in our literature and culture.

Frederick Douglass was reminding antebellum America of the virtue of independence when he wrote:

> "I have said that the Declaration of Independence is the ring-bolt to the chain of your nation's destiny; so, indeed, I regard it. The principles contained in that instrument are saving principles. Stand by those principles, be true to them on all occasions, in all places, against all foes, and at whatever cost."

Susan B. Anthony distilled her fierce advocacy for women's rights into a three word epigram:

> "Independence is happiness."

Ayn Rand extended the reach of independence deep into the economic sphere:

> "Freedom (n.): To ask nothing. To expect nothing. To depend on nothing."

Virginia Woolf insisted that independence is critical to creative expression:

> "I will go on adventuring, changing, opening my mind and my eyes, refusing to be stamped

and stereotyped. The thing is to free one's self:
to let it find its dimensions, not be impeded."

THIS IS THE LIGHT.

And where there is light,
there we also find shadow.

American culture fosters an independent mode of
being that emphasizes the pursuit of personal goals
and an attendant feeling of self-efficacy. In fact, the
perception of "personal control" in daily life is the
strongest predictor of health and well-being in this
country.[1]

And concerning the loss of personal control...

When, at last, night comes;
we pray
we'll never be
a burden on those we love.

When, at last, sleep comes;
we dream
of a threadbare
independence.

The greater the esteem accorded to independence,
the greater the fear of its opposite.

CHAPTER IV
THE EXPECTATION OF INDEPENDENCE

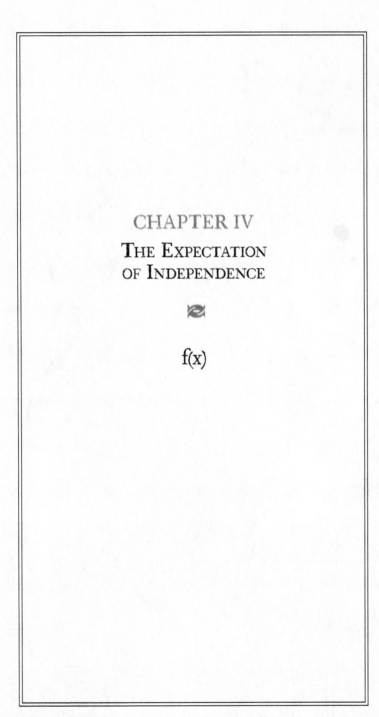

f(x)

The expectations that surround independence
are intense and intensely personal. We are all
participants in a distinctly modern mythology
that places autonomy at the heart of dignity. This
narrative defines personal control as a binary
variable:

$$\text{Independence} = 1$$
$$\text{and}$$
$$\text{Dependence} = 0$$

Rarely questioned cultural ideals reinforce the
belief that independence is the ideal state for every
person at every point on the lifespan.

We can express this ideal in the form of a simple
equation:

$$y = 1$$

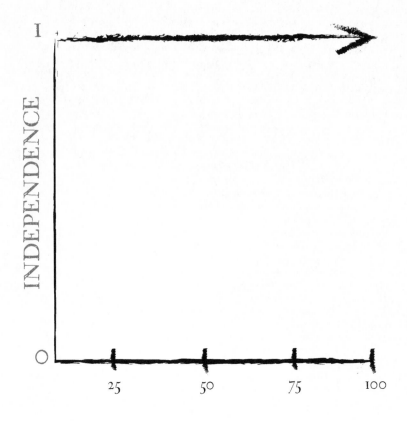

[Figure 7: The Ideal of Independence]

Just a bit of reflection, however, reveals important exceptions to the ideal of "independence" across the lifespan.

Minors, for example, can do many things for themselves but they are not considered to be "independent."

$$\text{When } x < 18$$
$$y = 0$$

It is not until we reach the "age of majority" that we gain our full legal rights and and become solely liable for our own actions.

$$\text{When } 18 < x < 98$$
$$\text{we expect that}$$
$$y = 1$$

$$\text{and}$$

The most long-lived among us are, thankfully, excused from the obligations that come with living as an independent adult.

$$\text{When } x > 98$$
$$y = 0$$

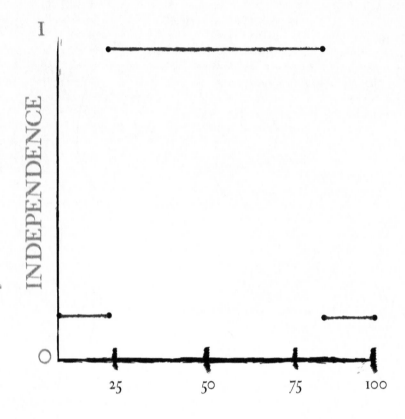

[Figure 8: Independence as a Binary Function]

We can create a graph that approximates our expectations of dependence and independence across the lifespan.

We will call the function that describes these expectations:

$$f(x)$$

Now that we have a model that describes how our expectations of independence change across the lifespan, we can turn our attention to age-related changes in the experience of independence.

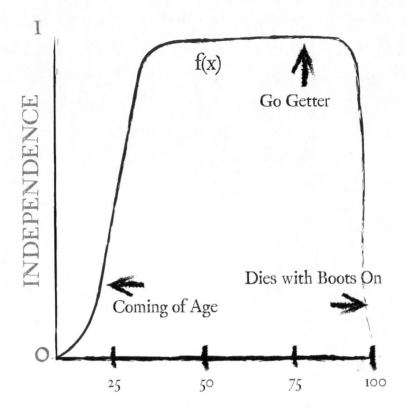

[Figure 9: The Expectation of Independence]

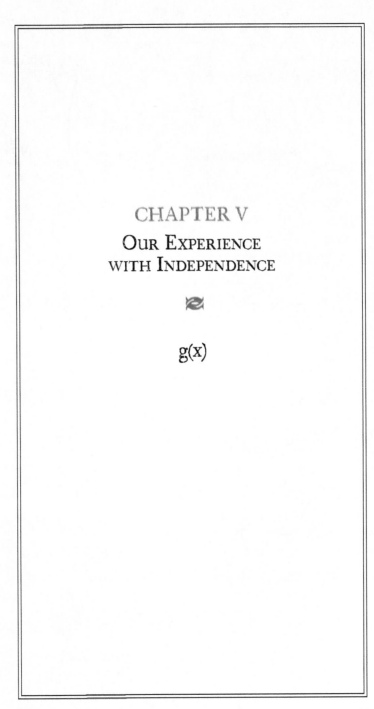

CHAPTER V

OUR EXPERIENCE
WITH INDEPENDENCE

g(x)

THREE DAYS IN MAY

The independence we covet is hard to win and very easy to lose.

On Friday actor Christopher Reeve's professional future shimmered with possibilities.

On Saturday equestrian Christopher Reeve's horse threw him during a competition in Culpeper, Virginia.

On Sunday quadriplegic Christopher Reeve was permanently placed on a ventilator. He would depend on one of these machines for the rest of his life.

38

Individuals cannot predict their
future experiences with dependence
and independence.

NOR, I SUSPECT, WOULD
THEY WANT TO.

We can, however, make strikingly accurate projections concerning how large populations will experience independence as they move across the lifespan.

We know, for example, that (as a population) children will exhibit relatively little variance in their experience with gaining independence.

Event	Typical Ages	Range
Weaning	3 mo. - 3 years	2-3 years
Start Schooling	3 - 5 years	2 years
Driver's License	16 - 20 years	4 years
Legal Majority	18 years	0 years

Older people, in contrast, exhibit a large amount of variance in their experience with dependence and independence.

Event	Typical Ages	Range
Retirement	50 - 75	25 years
Selling Family home	75 - 95	20 years
Surrender License	80 - 95	15 years
Death of Spouse	60 - 90	30 years

40

WE CAN USE THE WORD
"POLYMORPHISM" TO
DESCRIBE THIS AGE-RELATED
INCREASE IN VARIANCE.

There are scores of published volumes that detail the conflicted relationship that two-year olds' typically develop with dependence and independence.

It makes sense to us that there
would be a book titled:

MAKING THE "TERRIBLE"
TWOS TERRIFIC

But. We will never see a copy of:

MAKING THE "TERRIBLE"
EIGHTY-TWOS TERRIFIC

Age-related polymorphism will always ensure that there is no such thing as a typical 82-year-old.

In graph form, polymorphism looks like this...

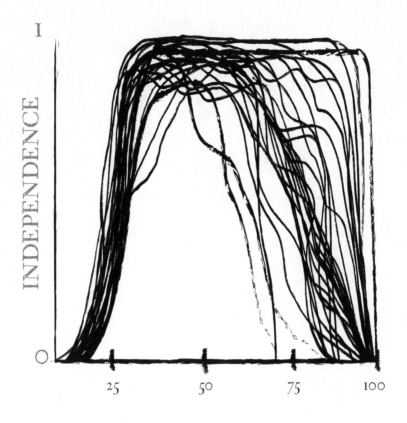

[Figure 10: Varied Experiences with Independence]

43

Because this work addresses aging at the population-level, we will create a single line that describes these experiences. We will call this function:

$$g(x)$$

TRANSLATION:
Changes in life stages are defined by changes in our experience of independence—whether we like that, or not.

We are now ready to plot our shared expectations about independence

$$f(x)$$

alongside our general experience with independence

$$g(x).$$

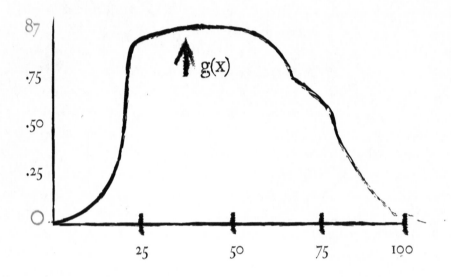

[Figure II: The Mean Experience of Independence]

CHAPTER VI
DISTRESSING GAPS

$$f(x) > g(x)$$

In a perfect world, expectations of a healthy independence would be high and our lived experience would come very close to matching them.

We do not, however, live in a perfect world.

EXPERIENCES

≠

EXPECTATIONS

Anyone who has ever gone on a blind date knows how distressing it can be when an experience fails to meet our expectations.

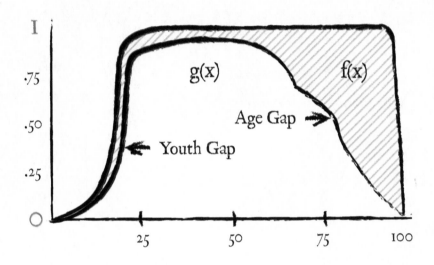

[Figure 12: Experience with and Expectations
of Independence]

THE YOUTH GAP:

When x<25
g(x) < f(x)

$$\text{Youth Gap} = \int_{0}^{50} f(x) - g(x) \, d(x)$$

TRANSLATION:

Young people often seek more independence
than they are allowed to have.

Our society works hard to narrow the "Youth Gap."

We collectively push experiences closer to expectations
by actively preparing young people for an independent
adulthood.

Young people living with developmental disabilities
are excused from the moral obligation of attaining
full independence.

The few young people who choose to be "dependent"
are labelled as failures and derided for their failure
to "grow up."

THE AGE GAP:

For x>50
f(x)>g(x)

$$\text{Age Gap} = \int_{50}^{100} f(x) - g(x) \, d(x)$$

TRANSLATION:
Many people find that, as they grow older, they experience less independence than they expected.

Efforts to narrow the Youth Gap align perfectly with our culture's devotion to youth and independence. The Age Gap, in contrast, is widened by ageism and commonly accepted stereotypes of loss and dependence in later life.

Contemporary American society awards worth, meaning and dignity primarily to those who continue to live in the manner of productive adults.

People who have retired from full-time paid employment understand this very well and are quick to remind friends and strangers alike that they've "never been so busy."

A compassionate people would release less vital elders from the obligations imposed by the adult role, but that rarely happens, in practice. Indeed, older people often feel compelled to hide evidence of their diminished reserve capacity.

People of all ages understand very well that the highest praise is reserved for those whom time changes the least. The idealization of "successful aging" leads directly to the tyranny of "still."

AT 82, JANE SMITH
STILL WALKS
THREE MILES
EVERY MORNING.

Deviations from the parameters of vigorous adulthood are marked as evidence of personal and, very likely, moral failure. Indeed, the word "still" serves as a linguistic whip whose stripes enforce a fierce doctrine. "Still" insists that:

Youth
will ever
and always be
superior to age.

We are all witnesses to a world-historic achievement. We have made what was once a rarity—entry into old age—into something that is ordinary. Hundreds of millions of people expect to grow old and will very likely do so. Even better, we have fashioned an old age that routinely yields the happiest years of one's life.

At the same time, we work ceaselessly to snatch defeat from the jaws of this great victory.

The success of human aging, which should be a cause for celebration, is dismissed as an expensive, undignified, and ultimately doomed, struggle against decline.

And nobody wants that.

THE TIME HAS COME TO
CHANGE AGING.

CHAPTER VII
THE RIGHT SHIFT

$$h(x)-g(x)>0$$

The Age Gap is a large, and largely invisible, source of distress for millions of Americans.

We relieve that distress whenever and wherever we are able to push the experience of aging closer to our expectation of independence.

This ambition can be expressed by transforming the function g(x).

When $x > 50$

$$h(x) = g(x) + a$$

when a is positive

$$h(x) - g(x) > 0$$

TRANSLATION:
Increasing reserve capacity increases the health span and can move older people toward a higher level of independence.

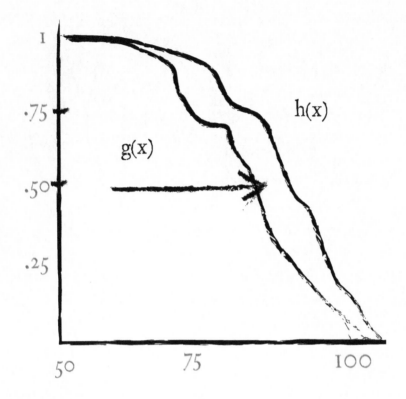

[Figure 13: **The Right** Shift

Shifting the Experience curve to the right expands
and enhances independence and the perception of
personal control.

Many of the bio-medical interventions proposed to explicitly boost the vitality of older people remain unproven and all lie outside the scope of this work.

Fortunately, we have ready access to a common sense strategy for accomplishing the same goal.

Reserve capacity (the bag of gold coins) is strongly influenced by a relationship known as:

PERSON-ENVIRONMENT FIT

All environments, at all times, vary in the amount of stress they apply to the creatures that inhabit them. This is known as "environmental press."

The principle of polymorphism reminds us that, especially where elders are concerned, the needs and capacities of the "person" in the person-environment equation vary widely.

ENVIRONMENTAL PRESS IS A GOLDILOCKS PHENOMENON.

When environmental press is insufficient, people experience the loss of function over time.

Even though astronauts in space work hard to maintain muscle mass, they always return to earth with significantly reduced strength and endurance.

When environmental press is excessive, reserve capacity is drained away. Elite marathon runners are exquisitely sensitive to air temperature and humidity. Their performance degrades quickly whenever conditions vary significantly from the ideal.

**Not too much,
not too little,
environmental press needs to be
— just right.**

Far from getting it "just right," our society pays little heed to the person-environment fit experienced by elders in their daily lives.

WHY DOES SOMETHING SO IMPORTANT SEEM TO MATTER SO LITTLE?

The answer lies in a self-fulfilling prophesy.

Despite the historic size of the opportunity and an extraordinary level of unmet need, fields related to aging have seen remarkably little innovation.

An innovation deficit condemns millions of older people to circumstances defined by poor person-environment fit.

Living with an unhealthy level of environmental press (too much or too little) accelerates the loss of reserve capacity and resilience.

What is actually a pathological loss of function is normalized by a caricature that depicts older people as being naturally frail and helpless.

The constant reinforcement of a narrative of decline validates ageist prejudices and diminishes the drive for innovation.

Repeat.

Properly matching environmental press to the needs and capacities of the person conserves reserve capacity and improves resilience.

The ability to alter the press created by a range of environments quickly and accurately and, in doing so, optimize them for different individuals at different points in time is valuable.

The ability to offer people living with a limited reserve capacity personal control over the press created by the environment in which they find themselves living is exceptionally valuable.

The development of products and services that facilitate the skillful management of environmental press could transform the lives of hundreds of millions of older people living near the boundary that defines dependence and independence.

CHAPTER VIII
THE LEFT SHIFT

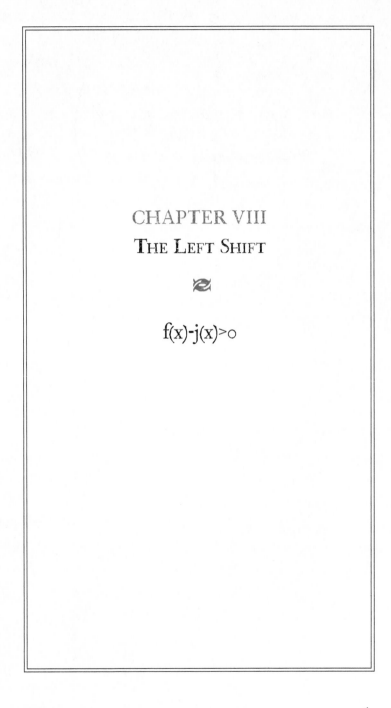

$$f(x)-j(x)>0$$

We can also increase the well-being of older people by shifting our culture's expectations about independence to the left.

Transforming the function g(x) allows us to express this ambition mathematically:

$$\text{When } x > 50$$

$$j(x) = f(x) - b$$

when b is positive

$$\int_{50}^{100} f(x) - j(x)\ d(x) > 0$$

TRANSLATION:
Pushing the expectation of independence closer to elders' experience with independence reduces the pain caused by the Age Gap.

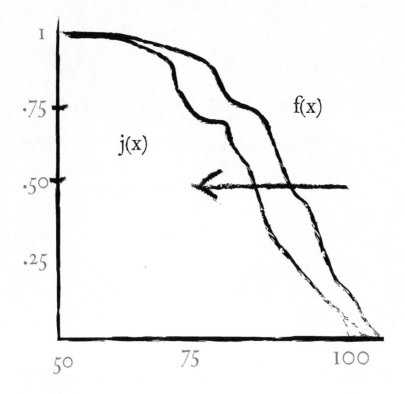

[Figure 14: The Left Shift

WE CHANGE
EXPECTATIONS
ABOUT
INDEPENDENCE
WHEN WE...

Defang Ageism

Foster Reciprocity

Normalize Polymorphism

Ageism leads us to judge others according to their chronological age rather than by their individual merits. While ageism can be directed at the young as well as the old, this work is primarily concerned with the impact of negative ageism directed at older people.

SLUR:

an insinuation or allegation about
someone that is likely to insult them
or damage their reputation.

Racist slurs and sexist slurs are no longer spoken aloud in polite company but we are exposed to ageist slurs almost every day.

The word "elderly" is an ageist slur because it refers exclusively to negative stereotypes of older people. People use this word to describe others, never themselves.

We begin to defang ageism when we challenge the casual age-related bigotry that populates so many conversations with and about older people.

No more black balloons.

IT IS SAID THAT PLEASURE
MAY RELY UPON ILLUSION, BUT
HAPPINESS REQUIRES THE TRUTH.

The truth is that we live by and through ceaseless cooperation with others. The pursuit of reciprocity in our relationships with others is a cultural and biological universal. Human dignity should be defined by relationships, not function.

ILLUSION:
Being independent means relying as little as possible on other people.

TRUTH:
Being independent means having control over the manner in which one cooperates with others.

ILLUSION:
To be dependent is to be compelled to rely on others for basic daily needs.

TRUTH:
To be dependent is to be human. We all rely on others for the necessities of life. It is the form which this reliance takes that determines our sense of well-being.

Millennia ago, Cicero wrote:

> "There is no duty more indispensable than that of returning a kindness. All men distrust one forgetful of a benefit."

The contemporary approach to aging too often disempowers and isolates older people and, in doing so, makes it especially difficult for them to "return a kindness."

Acknowledging the bedrock truth that we are all simultaneously independent and dependent can lead us toward a deeper understanding of our intensely social nature.

INTERDEPENDENCE: As human beings, we live by and through ceaseless cooperation with others—it is our destiny. We grow, mature, and then age and, at every point along this journey, our well-being is tightly interwoven with that of those around us. Aging changes the nature, not the fact, of our reliance on others.

AGING IS THE ULTIMATE
TEAM SPORT.

VIEWING INNOVATION
THROUGH THE LENS OF
RECIPROCITY CAN HELP
US RE-EVALUATE SEEMINGLY
ORDINARY OPPORTUNITIES.

No one would be surprised to learn that a local senior center was installing new technology for the use of its members.

BUT WHAT IF...

That same center had arranged to make their new equipment and software available to school children and, in doing so, worked to close the "digital divide."

BETTER.

What if the school district and senior center collaboratively organized a joint educational program designed to leverage the new technology and tools in ways that foster intergenerational relationships and reciprocity for the entire community?

BEST.

Community is the killer app.

The principle of polymorphism offers a direct challenge to our culture's understanding of the nature of aging. We are told that old age is a time of dull conformity. We are told that aging narrows our range of experiences and diminishes our value. In fact, the opposite is true.

AGING CREATES A WEALTH OF DIFFERENCES.

Most four year-olds are about forty inches tall and weigh about forty pounds.

Most eight-four year-olds are...quite different from other eighty-four olds.

Because there can never be a single answer to the many difficulties that arise from being part of a family and community, we will always need access to a variety of insights and perspectives.

Elders are valuable precisely because their lived experience is so wide ranging. Taken together, the insights gained by elders as individuals form a kind of cultural commons.

There is a word that describes biological processes capable of yielding development and differentiation over time. The word is "growth."

Decline travels only a few well-worn pathways. Growth creates and expands upon differences.

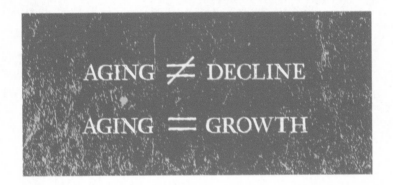

AGING ≠ DECLINE

AGING = GROWTH

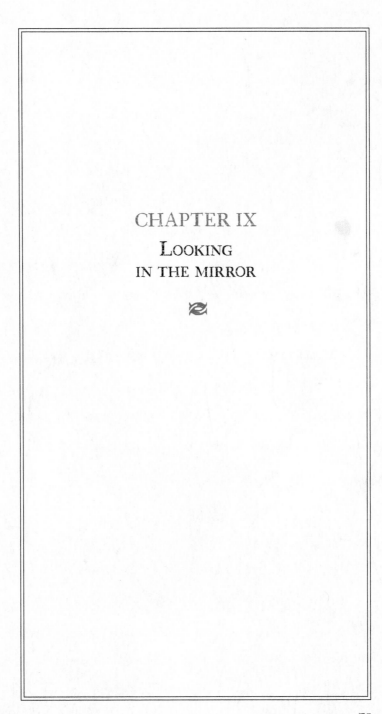

CHAPTER IX

Looking
in the mirror

Aging has always been about "them." They are getting old. They need help.

Slowly, fitfully, a new perspective is beginning to emerge. The new story is about us. We are aging—and that is a good thing.

But nothing this big or this important comes easily.

We've been told that aging creates flaws and that our wrinkles, creases, and blemishes are evidence of our decline.

WHAT IF...

We learned a new way to look into the mirror? The face we see there could show us a new way to age.

The shame-based approach to aging is reinforced by a mediascape that loudly and insistently proclaims,

"You are young!"

"Youth is always better than age!"

"You can be young forever!"

In public, we say, "You are as young as you feel..."

In private we can feel the truth, we are aging.

Despite what we've been told, it is within our power to look into a mirror, study what we see there, and acknowledge, without reservation, that we are no longer young.

We can learn to read the story of our lives as it has been written around our eyes and mouth and across our foreheads and cheeks. We can begin to reinterpret the changes as signs of important signifiers of our unique journey through life.

Rejecting this mythology and embracing aging can be painful, but we must do so if we want to continue growing. The best place to start this exercise in truth-telling is in front of a mirror.

ANY MIRROR CAN SHOW US THE TRUTH— IF WE ARE WILLING TO SEE IT.

It is time to have a private conversation with your own true self.

Stand before a mirror.

If you are young, you can absorb the truth that youth is a fleeting state and should be enjoyed fully, while it lasts.

If you are no longer young, you can make peace with the changes you see on your face and feel in your mind and body. You are better, different, changing, growing, learning— you are on your way to a new way of living.

This path to personal fulfillment includes just two steps:

1. STOP PINING FOR WHAT IS PAST.

2. START SEARCHING FOR THE PERSON YOU ARE MEANT TO BECOME.

The unyielding realities of biology, demography, and history are poised to incinerate the comforting illusion that "adulthood can last forever, if you want it to." Our next great cultural challenge will require us to build a society that values both youth and age, strength and frailty.

PEOPLE ARE ALREADY BEGINNING TO ENVISION WAYS OF LIVING THAT RIPPLE WITH BEAUTY, WORTH, AND MEANING— AT EVERY AGE.

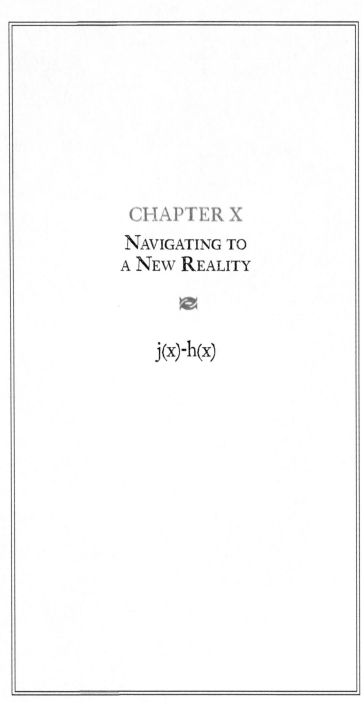

CHAPTER X

NAVIGATING TO
A NEW REALITY

$j(x)-h(x)$

"And all I ask is a tall ship and a star to
steer her by..." John Masefield

Elderhood was created, protected, nurtured and sustained because it serves vital human interests. We are heading into an era of unprecedented human longevity and a historic responsibility now rests on our shoulders. It has fallen to us to create a new elderhood, one that suits the way we live now.

Those who would dare to change aging must first seek to understand its true nature. As we have seen, aging is a process that resists easy categorization. It is not one thing. It is many things. Given this complexity, some have found it useful to employ a metaphor that presents human aging as a complex triple-alloy consisting of:

the Person

+

Technology

+

the Culture

Just as with metal alloys, each element interacts with and alters the attributes of the others.

Innovators working in fields related to aging often err by concentrating exclusively on just one or two terms in the following equation.

Personal Change +
Technological Change +
Cultural Change ➔ Impact on Expectations +
Impact on Experience ➔ Total Impact

Expressed mathematically, it looks like this:

Total Impact =

$$\int_{50}^{100} [f(x) - j(x)] + [h(x) - g(x)] \, d(x)$$

TRANSLATION:
Narrowing the age gap requires us to change the experience of aging and our expectations of independence. Concentrating on just one tool or one approach diminishes our ability to disrupt the status quo.

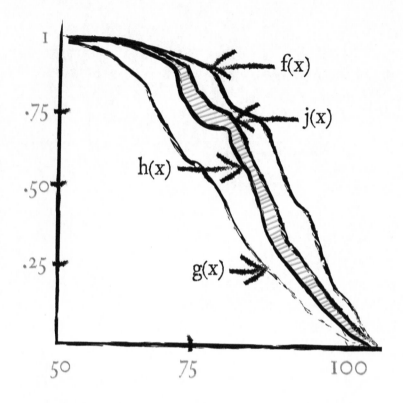

[Figure 15: Changing Aging]

So far, our focus has been on the means by and through which we might change aging. Now we must ask how the success or failure of such efforts might be measured.

NOT ALL CHANGE, IT SEEMS, IS EQUALLY DESIRABLE.

For example, the Age Gap could be decisively closed by destroying older people's expectations of independence. It is terribly easy, after all, to meet expectations that have been set extremely low. Such a massive lowering of expectations would, however, also make people much less, rather than more happy.

Long-term success in this arena will depend on the ability to link the impact of innovation directly to positive changes in well-being.

There are those who question the practicality of measuring something as elusive and deeply personal as well-being.

THIS IS NO LONGER A VALID OBJECTION.

Decades of research on well-being has coalesced around three powerful understandings:

STRENGTH— We need strength to live life on our own terms.

PURPOSE— Life matters little to those who can no longer grasp the reason they are in this world.

BELONGING— Relationships, and the communities that arise from relationships, are the most most reliable of all human shelters.

Each of these elements is well understood and each is within our reach, if not always our grasp.

These virtues must guide us as we narrow the distance between what is and what ought to be.

WHAT IS...

When researchers ask people where they would like to live as they grow older, the answer is unequivocal.

People want to remain in their own homes, no matter what. "Aging in place" is the triple-distilled essence of the American dream of aging with independence and dignity.

The problem is that aging in place offers no guarantees. In fact, research shows that a significant number of older people living alone at home struggle with loneliness, social isolation, under-nutrition, and increased exposure to emotional and financial exploitation. People believe, contrary to all available evidence, that as they grow older:

PLACE >> RELATIONSHIPS

When we step outside the reality distortion field created by "aging in place" rhetoric we find that almost all of the people who have ever grown old (on every continent and in every era) have done so in the company of kith and kin.

WHAT OUGHT TO BE...

Aging is, and will always remain a team sport. The value of aging within a community rich in authentic personal relationships vastly outweighs that of "hanging on to the house," even if that means moving out of one's current dwelling.

This is called "aging in community."

Our independence revolution depends on close and continuing intergenerational relationships. People who age in community are positioned to play vital roles in this exchange and, in doing so, connect us to our past, our present, and our future.

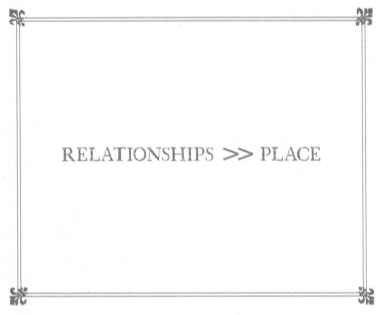

RELATIONSHIPS >> PLACE

WHAT IS...

When an older person needs help with the activities of daily living, we call the assistance provided to them "caregiving." Family members are often called upon to do this work and most undertake it without training, compensation (other than the emotional rewards) or respite. In Western societies caregiving is most often carried out within a social dyad.

One person is defined as the caregiver; the other is the "recipient of care." One person always gives; the other always receives.

Caregiver ➔ Recipient of Care

This is not healthy.

At its worst, this dyad breeds the fatigue, frustration and resentment that can lead to the abuse and neglect of elders by the very people who love them most.

WHAT OUGHT TO BE...

A growing chorus is beginning to challenge traditional ideas about intergenerational interdependence.

There is a growing reform movement that aims to replace the caregiving dyad with a team-oriented approach called "care partnering."

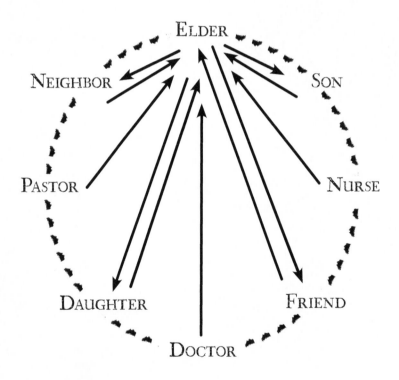

[Figure 16: Care-Partner Circle]

The elder is a member of the team and both gives and receives care. The experience of caring is shared among people who have different skills, insights, gifts and talents.

WHAT IS...

The medical profession is waking up to something that elders, and their families, already know all too well.

In 2013, Dr. Harlan Krumholz published an editorial in the New England Journal of Medicine that addressed the growing problem of "post-hospital" syndrome. He observed that older people being released from America's hospitals are:

> "...commonly deprived of sleep, experience disruption of normal circadian rhythms, are nourished poorly, have pain and discomfort, confront a baffling array of mentally challenging situations, receive medications that can alter cognition and physical function, and become deconditioned by bed rest or inactivity."

Far too often, older people are being subjected to a cure that is worse than the disease.

Nursing homes also routinely place tasks ahead of people and, in doing so, cultivate one of the most fearsome reputations on the public record. Surveys routinely reveal that elders fear life in a nursing home more than death.

Institutions deliver individualized care about as well as dogs walk on their hind legs. As Samuel Johnson observed about bipedal canines,

"It is not done well; but you are surprised to find it done at all."

WHAT OUGHT TO BE...

The era of mass institutionalization is, thankfully, drawing to a close. Ahead, we can already see the outlines of exciting innovations capable of supporting older people effectively wherever they choose to live.

This next generation of innovation will leverage disruptive insights into the personal experience of aging, advances in digital technology, and the effective promotion of a new cultural narrative that normalize growth and development across the lifespan.

WHAT IS...

Perhaps the best place to launch an independence revolution is with an attack on the persistent and pernicious practice of age segregation.

In 1954, the United States Supreme Court unanimously declared that "separate educational facilities are inherently unequal." Now, more than 60 years later, we find that millions of older people find themselves living in settings segregated by age and ability.

Our society's tendency to segregate people by age isn't confined to older people. We rigorously sort young people by age and ability and do so from the very beginning of their schooling. Not only are younger Americans isolated from elders, they are separated from people just a year or two older or younger than themselves, and in most cases from those with different abilities.

All of this is about to change.

SEGREGATING PEOPLE WITH
DIFFERING ABILITIES HARMS
PEOPLE OF ALL ABILITIES.

SEGREGATING PEOPLE OF
DIFFERENT AGES HARMS YOUNG
AND OLD.

SEGREGATING PEOPLE WITH
DIFFERENT BACKGROUNDS HARMS
PEOPLE OF ALL KINDS.

SEGREGATING PEOPLE HARMS
PEOPLE.

WHAT OUGHT TO BE...

MAGIC brings together people of many different abilities and generations and helps them create inclusive communities they love. These communities have the power to change people's expectations about aging and their experience with longevity.

Disrupting conventional understandings of aging and replacing them with a radical reinterpretation of longevity and community will connect people of all ages directly to a collective pursuit of happiness and well-being.

We will build our future here.

Multi-

Ability, multi-

Generational

Inclusive

Communities

THERE IS A NEW OLD AGE
WAITING TO BE BORN...

AND WE WILL
BE ITS MIDWIVES.

WILLIAM H. THOMAS, MD

Dr. Bill Thomas is a geriatrician with a quarter century of experience with creating and replicating new approaches to health and well being. Starting in the early 1990's he co-founded the Eden Alternative (with his wife Jude Meyers Thomas). This approach brought plants, animals, children, and news ways of living and working, into sterile nursing homes and soon spread around the world. In the early 2000's he developed the Green House (™) model that allowed older people living with frailty to become part of an household of ten to twelve people and share meals at a big wooden table. In the late 2000's he created the first emergency department for seniors, now considered the industry standard.

Dr. Thomas' latest project, Minka Homes and Communities, is focused on helping people of all ages live where and how they wish. The deceptively simple design of Minka is based on research into human complexity and decades of input from some of our culture's most vulnerable people. Dr. Thomas has distilled these insights into the Minka Building System. Minka blends centuries old Japanese joinery techniques with robot-driven manufacturing tools.

The result is a flexible, adaptable building system with components that can be combined and recombined to create millions of possible floorplans. Even better, this approach slashes waste and reduces the energy used by the building. Minka has also inspired a new community-building model called MAGIC being developed in partnership with the University of Southern Indiana and AARP. MAGIC stands for Multi-Ability, multi-Generational, Inclusive Communities.